Learnin Together

Illustrated by
Angela Mills

Brimax . Newmarket . England

A B C

Aa

a is for **a**crobat

Is the acrobat wearing a hat?
What else can you find that starts with **a**?

6

Bb

b is for **b**icycle

Which bicycle is blue?
What else can you find that starts with **b**?

Cc

c is for **c**at

What time does the clock say?
What else can you find that starts with **c**?

Dd

d is for **d**olphin

Point to the dog in the picture.
What else can you find that starts with **d**?

Ee

e is for **e**lephant

What is the elephant holding in his trunk?
What else can you find that starts with **e**?

Ff

f is for **f**air

Where is the merry-go-round?
What else can you find that starts with **f**?

Gg

g is for **g**loves

Who is wearing red gloves?
What else can you find that starts with **g**?

Hh

h is for **h**olly

Point to the holly in the picture.
What else can you find that starts with **h**?

13

Ii

i is for igloo

Who is eating ice-cream?
What else can you find that starts with **i**?

Jj

j is for **j**uggler

What is the juggler juggling with?
What else can you find that starts with **j**?

Kk

k is for **k**angaroo

Who is flying the kite?
What else can you find that starts with **k**?

Ll

l is for lake

How many boats are there on the lake?
What else can you find that starts with l?

17

Mm

m is for **m**ouse

Who is wearing mittens?
What else can you find that starts with **m**?

Nn

n is for **n**est

How many birds are in the nest?
What else can you find that starts with **n**?

Oo

o is for **o**wl

Can you see the owl?
What else can you find that starts with **o**?

Pp

p is for **p**icnic

How many plates are there?
What else can you find that starts with **p**?

21

Qq

q is for **q**ueen

Who is hiding under the quilt?
What else can you find that starts with **q**?

Rr

r is for **r**iver

Can you see the rainbow?
What else can you find that starts with **r**?

Ss

s is for **s**andcastle

How many sandcastles can you count?
What else can you find that starts with **s**?

24

Tt

t is for **t**rumpet

Who is playing the trumpet?
What else can you find that starts with **t**?

Uu

u is for **u**mbrella

How many rabbits are under the umbrella?
What else can you find that starts with **u**?

Vv

v is for **v**iolin

How many flowers are in the vase?
What else can you find that starts with **v**?

Ww

w is for **w**ig-wam?

Who is hiding in the wig-wam?
What else can you find that starts with **w**?

Xx

x is for **x**ylophone?

Who is playing the xylophone?
What else can you find that starts with **x**?

Yy

y is for **y**acht

How many rabbits are on the yacht?
What else can you find that starts with **y**?

Zz

z is for **z**ebra

What is the zebra doing?
What else can you find that starts with **z**?

1 2 3

1

one candle

It is Rosie Rabbit's birthday. She has one candle on her cake. All her friends are at the party.

How many candles are on the cake?

2

two bicycles

Rosie and Rags Rabbit are on a bike ride. They are racing each other. Who do you think will win?

How many bicycles are in the picture?

3

three balloons

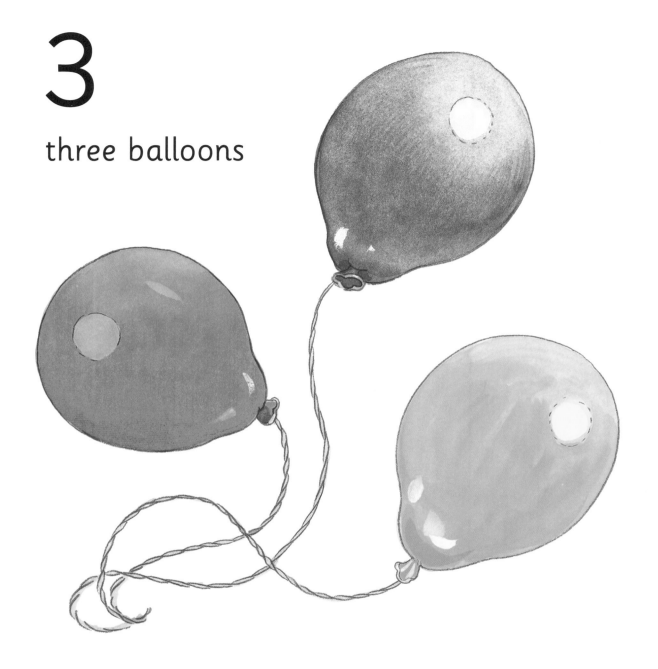

Mr and Mrs Rabbit have taken Rosie, Roly and Rags
to the fair. Mr Rabbit buys three balloons and
gives them to his children.

How many balloons does Mr Rabbit buy?

39

4

four flags

The rabbits are enjoying themselves at the beach. They have built four sandcastles and have put a flag on top of each one.

How many flags are in the picture?

41

5

five balls

The rabbits are at the circus. They are watching
the juggler. Roly thinks the juggler is very
clever to be able to juggle with five balls.

How many balls is the juggler juggling with?

6

six apples

Mrs Rabbit is at the shops with Rosie, Roly and Rags. She buys six apples and gives them to the rabbits to hold.

How many apples does Mrs Rabbit buy?

7

seven crayons

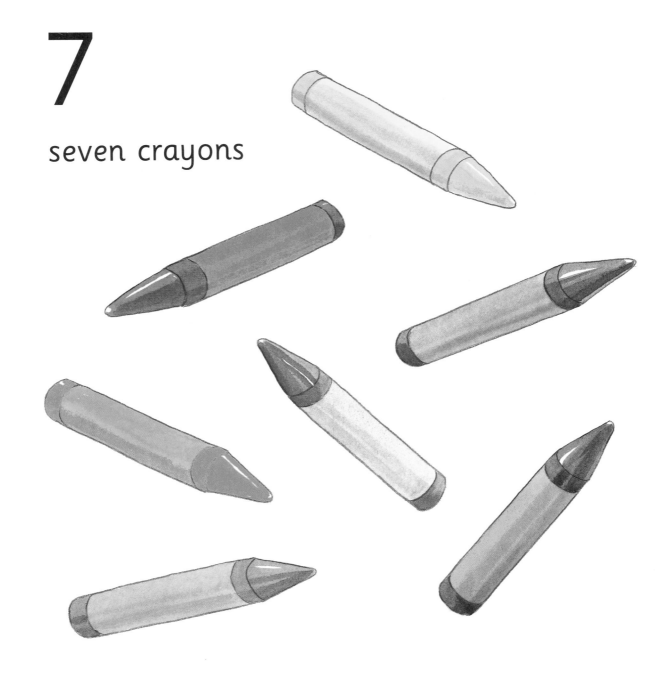

Rosie, Roly and Rags are drawing a picture. They have seven crayons. Rosie draws a yellow sun. Rags draws a green tree and Roly draws a blue river.

How many crayons do the rabbits have?

8

eight blocks

Rosie, Roly and Rags are playing in their room. They have built a tower with eight blocks. It is very tall.

How many blocks do the rabbits have?

9

nine chicks

Mr and Mrs Rabbit have taken Rosie, Roly and Rags to the farm. Rosie likes the fluffy chicks the best. There are nine altogether.

50 How many chicks are there on the farm?

10

ten stars

It is time for Rosie, Roly and Rags to go to bed.
They are looking out of the window and are
counting the stars. They can see ten stars.

How many stars can the rabbits see?

Find and Say

Rosie, Roly and Rags are playing with their toys.
The jack-in-the-box is square.

56 What else is square?

The rabbits are playing in the garden. They are
playing with Rosie's ball. Rosie's ball is red.
58 What else is red?

Rosie, Roly and Rags are at school. They are
watching their teacher. He is writing on the
blackboard. The blackboard is a rectangle.
60   What else is a rectangle?

Mr and Mrs Rabbit have taken Rosie, Roly and Rags to a farm. Rags thinks the tractor is great. The tractor is green.

What else is green?

It is Roly Rabbit's birthday. He is having a
party. His friends have brought him a present. The
present is round.

64 What else is round?

Mr and Mrs Rabbit have taken Rosie, Roly and Rags
to the sea-side. They are looking at the boats.
The biggest boat is blue.
What else is blue?

Mrs Rabbit has taken Rosie, Roly and Rags to the
park. Rags is flying his kite. His kite is
diamond-shaped.

68   What else is diamond-shaped?

Mr and Mrs Rabbit have taken Rosie, Roly and Rags
on a picnic. Rags has a yellow plate.

70 What else is yellow?

Roly is building a house with his blocks. The roof
of the house is a triangle.

72 What else is a triangle?

Read to Me

Mr and Mrs Rabbit are out in the garden.
Rags, Roly and Rosie are helping them.
"I wish I could have my own garden," says Rosie. "Then I could grow my own carrots!"
"I will help you," says Roly.
"And me!" says Rags.

Mr Rabbit laughs and says,
"You can have a piece of this
garden if you promise to look
after it!"
"Oh, thank you!" say Rosie,
Rags and Roly.
Mr Rabbit shows them the piece
of garden they can have.

Rosie picks up a little shovel and starts to dig. Rags starts to pull out the weeds and Roly holds the bucket.

Soon their little garden is ready for some seeds.

"Please can we have some carrot seeds?" they ask their father.

Mr Rabbit gives them a packet of carrot seeds.
"Thank you!" they say.
Rosie digs the holes, Roly puts in the seeds and Rags waters them. They like gardening.
"I cannot wait for the carrots to grow," says Rags.

The very next day, the three little rabbits run outside to look for carrots. They are disappointed when they cannot see anything.

"It will take a little longer than that for your carrots to grow," laughs Mr Rabbit.

Every day either Rosie, Roly or Rags check to see if the carrots have started to grow. One day Roly gives a shout, "I have found some carrots! Look Rosie and Rags!"
The two rabbits come running and sure enough, right in the middle of their little garden are some carrot stalks.

"Let's pull them out!" says Rags.
Rosie pulls all the carrots up but one will not move. Then Roly tries but he cannot move it either. The three rabbits all pull together and the biggest carrot ever comes out of the ground!

"Wow!" says Rags. "It's enormous!"
The three rabbits take the carrot to show their mother and father.
"Goodness me!" says Mrs Rabbit. "Did you grow that?"
"Yes!" says Rosie. "Does this mean we are good gardeners?"
"Very good ones!" laughs Mr Rabbit.

The three rabbits are very proud of themselves. They help their mother prepare the carrot for dinner. They are having carrot stew.

When they have eaten it they are all full. They all agree that Rosie, Roly and Rags grow the biggest carrots ever!